BOOK 2 - Tuba

STANDARD OF EXCELLENCE

COMPREHENSIVE BAND METHOD

By Bruce Pearson

Dear Student:

Congratulations! You have successfully attained the first level in achieving a standard of excellence in music-making. By now, you have discovered that careful study and regular practice have brought you the joy and satisfaction of making beautiful music.

You are now ready to move to the next level in your music-making. I want to welcome you to STANDARD OF EXCELLENCE Book 2. I also want to wish you continued success and enjoyment.

Best wishes,

Bruce Pearson

Practicing - the key to EXCELLENCE!

▶ Make practicing part of your daily schedule. If you plan practicing as you do any other activity, you will find plenty of time for it.
▶ Try to practice in the same place every day. Choose a place where you can concentrate on making music. Start with a regular and familiar warm-up routine, including long tones and simple technical exercises. Like an athlete, you need to warm-up your mind and muscles before you begin performing.
▶ Set goals for every practice session. Keep track of your practice time and progress on the front cover Practice Journal.
▶ Practice the hard spots in your lesson assignment and band music over and over, until you can play them perfectly.
▶ Spend time practicing both alone and with the STANDARD OF EXCELLENCE recorded accompaniments.
▶ At the end of each practice session, play something fun.

ISBN 0-8497-5967-6

© 1993 Neil A. Kjos Music Company, 4380 Jutland Drive, San Diego, California.
International copyright secured. All rights reserved. Printed in the U. S. A.

KJOS NEIL A. KJOS MUSIC COMPANY, PUBLISHER

W22BS

REVIEW

B♭ MAJOR KEY SIGNATURE

1 WARM-UP - Band Arrangement

2 B♭ MAJOR SCALE SKILL

▶ Lines with a medal are *Achievement Lines.* The chart on page 47 can be used to record your progress.

3 BOTANY BAY   Page 40 ▐▐▐▶

Australian Folk Song

▶ When you see a page number followed by an arrow, *Excellerate* to the page indicated for additional studies.

4 DRIVE TIME

5 SHEPHERD'S HEY

English Folk Song

REVIEW

E♭ MAJOR KEY SIGNATURE

6 E♭ MAJOR SCALE SKILL

Moderato , Arpeggio , Chords

mf

▶ Are you playing with a good embouchure and hand position?

7 MOLLY MALONE

Irish Folk Song

Andante

mp *f* *mp* *rit.* *mp*

8 NO LOOKING BACK

Page 40 ▶

Moderato

mf

9 TURKISH MARCH

Wolfgang Amadeus Mozart (1756 - 1791)

Allegro

mf

10 HYMN OF THANKSGIVING - Band Arrangement

Johann Crüger (1598 - 1662)
arr. Bruce Pearson (b. 1942)

Andante

mf *p* *mf*

p *f* *mf* *rit.*

REVIEW

F MAJOR KEY SIGNATURE

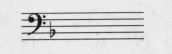

11 WARM-UP - Band Arrangement

Andante

12 F MAJOR SCALE SKILL

Moderato ... Arpeggio ... Chords

13 KNUCKLEBUSTER

Moderato

1. ... 2.

14 GIVE ME THAT OLD TIME RELIGION Page 40

American Spiritual

Allegro

clap

15 _____ Composer _____

your name

Moderato

▶ Compose an ending for this melody. Title and play your composition.

16 FOR TUBAS ONLY Page 40

Allegro

| SYNCOPATION |  | A rhythmic effect which places emphasis on a weak or unaccented part of the measure. |
| INTERVAL |  | The distance between any two notes. |

17 SYNCOPATION SENSATION

Moderato

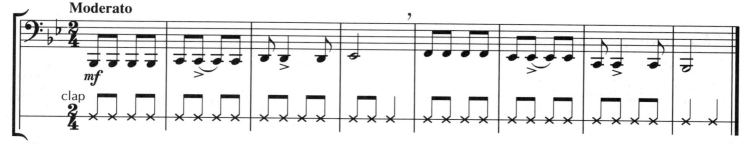

18 THE RIDDLE SONG

American Folk Song

Moderato

▶ Write in the counting and clap the rhythm before you play.

19 NOBODY KNOWS THE TROUBLE I'VE SEEN

American Spiritual

Moderato

20 INTERVAL INQUIRY

▶ Sing this exercise using the numbers before you play.

21 GO FOR EXCELLENCE!

American Folk Song

Allegro

"Liza Jane"

W22BS

DAL SEGNO AL FINE (D.S. AL FINE)

Go back to the sign (𝄋) and play until the *Fine*.

JOYEUX NOËL
Band Arrangement

French Carol
arr. Chuck Elledge (b. 1961)

29 **GO FOR EXCELLENCE!**

Ab MAJOR KEY SIGNATURE	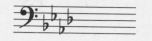	This key signature means play all B's as B flats, all E's as E flats, all A's as A flats, and all D's as D flats.
TEXTURES	**Monophony** - a single unaccompanied melody. **Polyphony** - two or more melodies played at the same time.	

36 Ab MAJOR SCALE SKILL

37 GREASED LIGHTNING

38 PARTNER SONGS - Duet

▶ For an example of monophony, play line A or line B alone. For an example of polyphony, play line A while someone else plays line B.

39 GO FOR EXCELLENCE!

Stephen Foster (1826 - 1864)

W22BS

ENHARMONICS

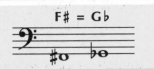

F# = Gb

Notes that sound the same but are written differently.

ARTICULATION

Staccato (dot placed above or below note) - Play short and detached.

TEMPO

Allegretto - light and lively; slightly slower than **Allegro.**

40 WARM-UP - Band Arrangement

Andante

mf

41 CHROMATIC CAPERS

Moderato   Gb

f   enharmonic   enharmonic

42 SHENANDOAH  **Page 40** ▶

American Folk Song

Andante

mp

43 THEME FROM SYMPHONY NO. 94

Franz Joseph Haydn (1732 - 1809)

Andante

p

44 PARADE OF THE TIN SOLDIERS

Léon Jessel (1871 - 1942)

Allegretto

mf

1.   2.

45 FOR TUBAS ONLY

Allegro

mf

TEXTURE	**Melody and Accompaniment** - main melody is accompanied by chords or less important melodies called **countermelodies.**

52 WARM-UP
Andante

53 HABAÑERA
Andante

Georges Bizet (1838 - 1875)

54 SMOOTH AS SILK
Allegretto

55 HEY HO - Round (Canon)

Page 41 ▶

Medieval Song

Allegro

56 THE BRITISH GRENADIERS - Duet

English Folk Song

Allegro
A. Melody

B. Countermelody

57 FOR TUBAS ONLY
Allegro

 **TIME SIGNATURE**

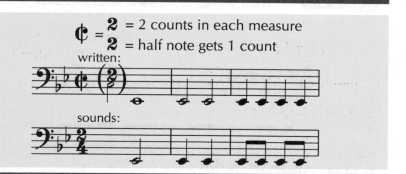

¢ = **2** = 2 counts in each measure
2 = half note gets 1 count
written:
sounds:

This time signature is called **cut time** or *alla breve.*

---

58 **CUT AND PASTE**

Moderato

▶ Write in the counting and clap the rhythm before you play.

59 **OATS, PEAS, BEANS**

American Folk Song

Moderato
A.
B.

60 **THE VICTORS**

Fight Song

Allegro

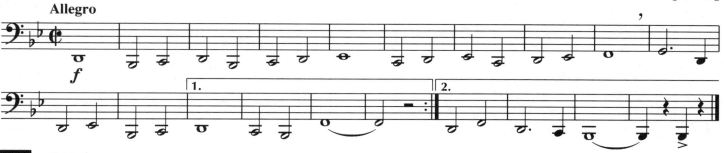

61 **OVER EASY**  **Page 41** ‖⟹

Andante

62 **GO FOR EXCELLENCE!**

John Philip Sousa (1854 - 1932)

Allegretto
"High School Cadets March"

14

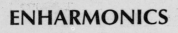 **ENHARMONICS**

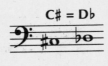

CHORD

Two or more pitches sounded at the same time.

63 **WARM-UP - Band Arrangement**

64 **DANISH ROLL**

Danish Folk Song

65 **RUSSIAN SAILORS' DANCE**

Reinhold Glière (1875 - 1956)

66 **CHORD CAPERS**

▶ Listen for the different types of chords played by the full band.

67 **FOR TUBAS ONLY**

ENHARMONICS

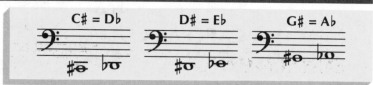

68 CHROMATIC SCALE SKILL

69 SAILING THE HIGH SEAS

70 CHROMATIC MARCH

Page 41

71 MANHATTAN BEACH MARCH

John Philip Sousa (1854 - 1932)

72 GO FOR EXCELLENCE!

Moderato

▶ Play using each of the following articulations: A. B. C. D.

DA CAPO AL CODA (D.C. AL CODA)

Go back to the beginning and play until the coda sign (⊕). When you reach the coda sign, skip to the **Coda** (⊕).

ROCK ISLAND EXPRESS
Band Arrangement

Chuck Elledge (b. 1961)

TIME SIGNATURE

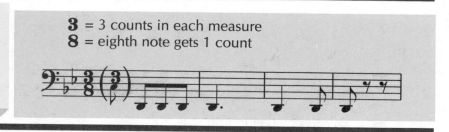

3 = 3 counts in each measure
8 = eighth note gets 1 count

---

73 FINLANDIA - Band Arrangement

Jean Sibelius (1865 - 1957)
arr. Bruce Pearson (b. 1942)

Permission granted for sale outside of the U.S.A. by Breitkopf & Härtel.
© Breitkopf & Härtel, Wiesbaden, Germany

74 TRIPLE PLAY

Allegretto

▶ Write in the counting and clap the rhythm before you play.

75 WE THREE KINGS

Page 41 ▐▐▐▐▶

John H. Hopkins, Jr. (1820 - 1891)

Andante

▶ Name the key in "We Three Kings." _____

76 GO FOR EXCELLENCE!

Allegro

 **C MAJOR KEY SIGNATURE**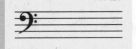

This key signature contains no sharps or flats.

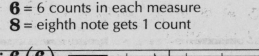 **TIME SIGNATURE** 6/8

6 = 6 counts in each measure
8 = eighth note gets 1 count

77 C MAJOR SCALE SKILL

78 OVER THE RIVER

Traditional

▶ Draw in a breath mark at the end of each phrase.

79 OODLES OF NOODLES

80 UPS AND DOWNS

▶ Write in the counting and draw in the bar lines before you play.

81 FOR TUBAS ONLY

W22BS

SIXTEENTH NOTES

Two sixteenth notes are as long as one eighth note.
Four sixteenth notes are as long as one quarter note.

$$\frac{1}{4} + \frac{1}{4} + \frac{1}{4} + \frac{1}{4} = \frac{1}{2} + \frac{1}{2} = 1 \text{ count}$$

Each sixteenth note gets ¼ count in $\frac{2}{4}$, $\frac{3}{4}$, and $\frac{4}{4}$ time.

82 WARM-UP - Band Arrangement

Andante

mf

23 _____

83 COUNT ME IN

Moderato

mf

▶ Write in the counting and clap the rhythm before you play.

84 KEMO KIMO

American Folk Song

Allegretto

p   *f*   *p*   *f*

p   *f*

85 FRENCH MARCHING SONG

French Folk Song

Allegro

1.   2.

f

▶ Name the interval between the first and second notes. _____

86 FENG YANG SONG   Page 41 ▐▌▌▌➡

Chinese Folk Song

Moderato

mp

87 GO FOR EXCELLENCE!

Patrick Gilmore (1829 - 1892)

Allegro

"When Johnny Comes Marching Home"

mp   *mf*

f   *mp*

88 **LOOBY LOO**

Anonymous

Name the key in "Looby Loo." _____

89 **THE THUNDERER**

John Philip Sousa (1854 - 1932)

90 **LISTEN TO THE MOCKINGBIRD**

Alice Hawthorne (1827 - 1902)

91 **GIVE MY REGARDS TO BROADWAY**

George M. Cohan (1878 - 1942)

92 **FOR TUBAS ONLY** Page 41 ➡

EIGHTH/SIXTEENTH NOTE COMBINATIONS

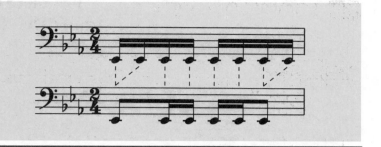

93 CHESTER - Band Arrangement

William Billings (1746 - 1800)
arr. Bruce Pearson (b. 1942)

94 STEADY AS YOU GO - Duet

95 TIRRA LIRRA LOO

Canadian Folk Song

▶ Write in the counting and clap the rhythm before you play.

96 GO FOR EXCELLENCE!

American Folk Song

Moderato

"Big Rock Candy Mountain"

TURKISH MARCH
from "The Ruins of Athens"
Solo with Piano Accompaniment

Ludwig van Beethoven (1770 - 1827)
arr. Bruce Pearson (b. 1942)

97 BLAZIN'

Moderato

mf

▶ Name the interval between the first and second notes. _____

98 AMERICAN PATROL

Frank W. Meacham (1856 - 1909)

Moderato

mp

to Coda

f *mp*

D.C. al Coda

Coda

f *mp*

99 KERRY DANCE **Page 41** ▮▮▮▶

Irish Folk Song

Moderato

mf

100 GAVOTTE

James Hook (1746 - 1827)

Andante

p

f

p

f

p

f

101 FOR TUBAS ONLY

Moderato

mf

1. 2.

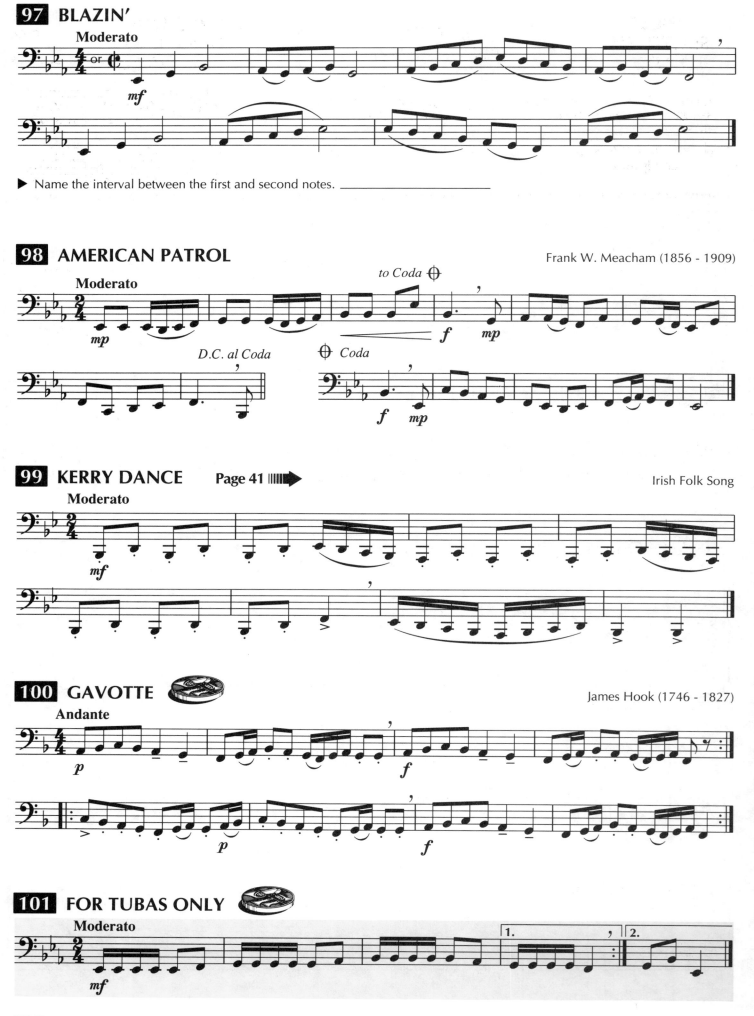

SINGLE SIXTEENTH NOTE

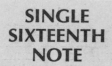

A single sixteenth note is half as long as an eighth note.

♬ = ¼ count in **2/2**, **3/4**, and **4/4** time.

DOTTED EIGHTH NOTE

A dot after a note adds half the value of the note.

♪ + • = ♪ + ♬ = ♪.

DOTTED EIGHTH/ SIXTEENTH NOTE COMBINATION

102 DOTS OF FUN

Moderato

103 LITTLE BROWN JUG - Duet

Joseph Eastburn Winner (1837 - 1918)

Allegro

▶ Write in the counting and clap the rhythm before you play.

104 OUR BOYS WILL SHINE TONIGHT

College Song

Allegretto

▶ Draw in a breath mark at the end of each phrase.

105 _____   Composer _____

your name

▶ Compose an ending for this melody. Be sure to use the rhythm. Title and play your composition.

106 GO FOR EXCELLENCE!

Georges Bizet (1838 - 1875)

Allegro

"Farandole from L'Arlesienne Suite"

26

Page 41

107 CUCKOO SONG

Austrian Folk Song

Andante

108 MARCH MILITAIRE

Franz Schubert (1797 - 1828)

Allegretto

to Coda ⊕

D.C. al Coda   ⊕ *Coda*

109 ST. ANTHONY CHORALE

Franz Joseph Haydn (1732 - 1809)

Andante

1.   2.   *Fine*

D.C. al Fine

110 _____   Composer _____

your name

a.   b.   c.   d.

▶ Arrange these melodic pieces in any order to build a tune you like. You may use pieces more than once. Title and play your composition.

111 FOR TUBAS ONLY

A Andante   B   C

▶ Play each of the lip slur patterns using the following fingerings: **0; 2; 1; 1 2; 2 3; 1 3; 1 2 3.**
You will be moving down a half step with each fingering.

EIGHTH NOTE TRIPLET

TEMPO

Maestoso - majestically

112 **TRIPLE TREAT**

Moderato

113 **STARS OF THE HEAVENS - Duet** Page 41

Mexican Folk Song

Allegro

114 **LIGHT CAVALRY OVERTURE**

Franz von Suppé (1819 - 1895)

Maestoso

115 **GO FOR EXCELLENCE!**

Charles Gounod (1818 - 1893)

Maestoso

"Soldiers' Chorus from Faust"

116 HERE WE COME A-WASSAILING

English Folk Song

117 THEME FROM "ZAMPA"

Ferdinand Herold (1791 - 1833)

118 GO FOR EXCELLENCE!

Peter Ilyich Tchaikovsky (1840 - 1893)

CABO RICO
Band Arrangement

Chuck Elledge (b. 1961)

W22BS

RUDIMENTAL REGIMENT

Band Arrangement

Bruce Pearson (b. 1942)
and Chuck Elledge (b. 1961)

SUMMER'S RAIN

Band Arrangement

Chuck Elledge (b. 1961)

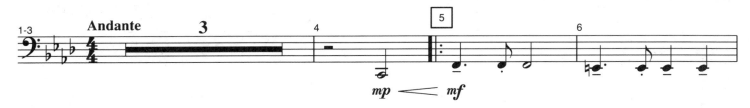

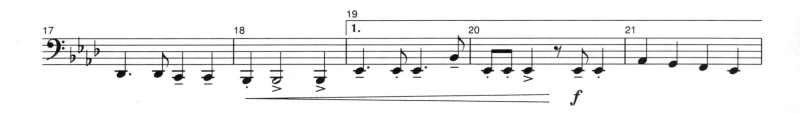

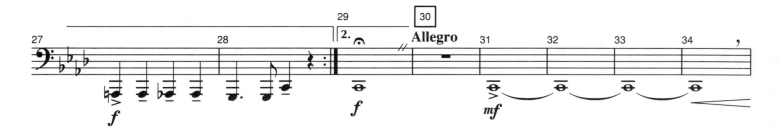

FRENCH MARKET BUZZARDS MARCH
Band Arrangement

Liberato Gallo
arr. Wendy Barden (b. 1955)

W22BS

ROMANZA

Ensemble

Tuba

Ludwig van Beethoven, Op. 40 (1770 - 1827)
arr. Janice Strobl Kersey (b. 1959)

HORNPIPE from "Water Music"

Ensemble

George Frideric Handel (1685 - 1759)
arr. Janice Strobl Kersey (b. 1959)

Tuba

MORNING SONG AND MARCH
from "Little Suite" for Solo Piano
Solo with Piano Accompaniment

Cornelius Gurlitt (1820 - 1901)
arr. Bruce Pearson (b. 1942)

EXCELLERATORS - FOR TUBAS ONLY

EXCELLERATORS-FOR TUBAS ONLY

▶ Play this lip slur pattern using the following fingerings:
0; 2; 1; 1 2; 2 3; 1 3; 1 2 3.
You will be moving down a half step with each fingering.

▶ Play this lip slur pattern using the following fingerings:
0; 2; 1; 1 2; 2 3; 1 3; 1 2 3.
You will be moving down a half step with each fingering.

SCALE STUDIES

B♭ MAJOR SCALE

G HARMONIC MINOR SCALE

E♭ MAJOR SCALE

C HARMONIC MINOR SCALE

SCALE STUDIES

F MAJOR SCALE

Ab MAJOR SCALE

C MAJOR SCALE

CHROMATIC SCALE

RHYTHM STUDIES

RHYTHM STUDIES

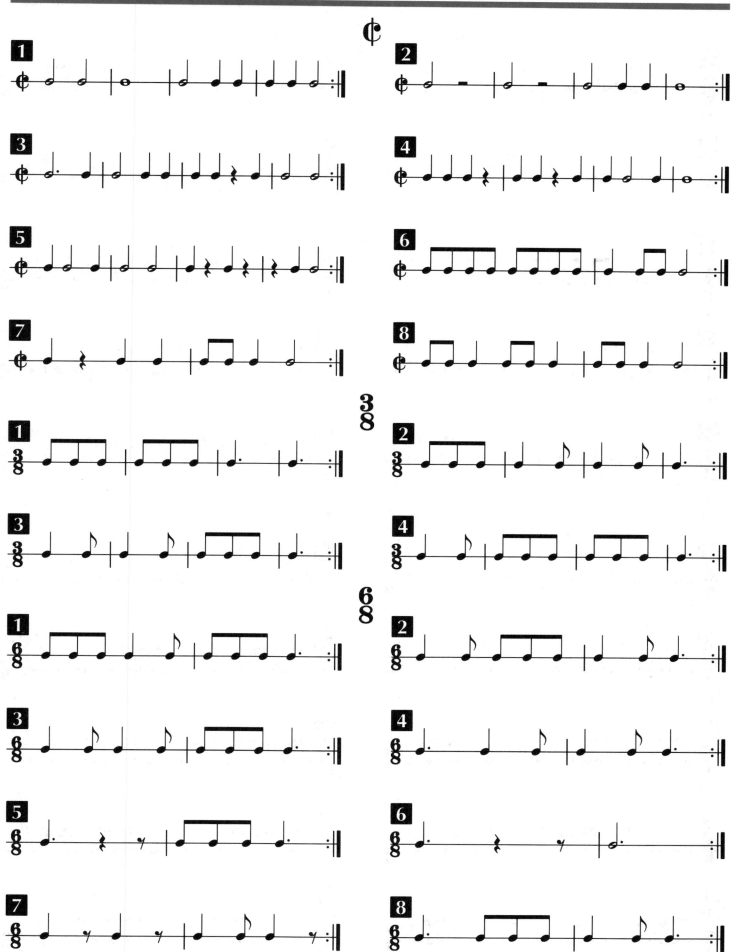
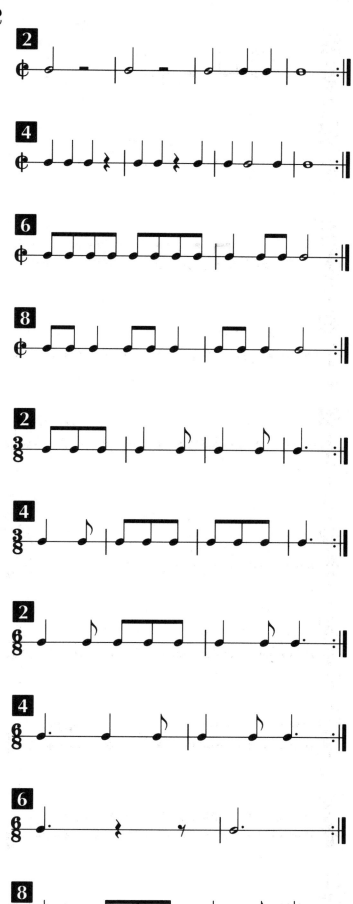

GLOSSARY/INDEX

STANDARD OF EXCELLENCE

EXERCISE 2
- [ ] notes/rhythm
- [ ] posture
- [ ] embouchure
- [ ] breathing

EXERCISE 5
- [ ] notes/rhythm
- [ ] dynamics
- [ ] articulations
- [ ] *D. C. al Fine*

EXERCISE 6
- [ ] notes/rhythm
- [ ] hand position
- [ ] breathing
- [ ] tone

EXERCISE 7
- [ ] notes/rhythm
- [ ] *ritardando*
- [ ] dynamics
- [ ] 1st/2nd endings

EXERCISE 12
- [ ] notes/rhythm
- [ ] posture
- [ ] hand position
- [ ] breathing

EXERCISE 16
- [ ] notes/rhythm
- [ ] embouchure
- [ ] hand position
- [ ] tone

EXERCISE 21
- [ ] notes/rhythm
- [ ] hand position
- [ ] dynamics
- [ ] tempo

EXERCISE 24
- [ ] notes/rhythm
- [ ] embouchure
- [ ] 𝄐
- [ ] tone

EXERCISE 28
- [ ] notes/rhythm
- [ ] posture
- [ ] hand position
- [ ] tone

EXERCISE 29
- [ ] notes/rhythm
- [ ] embouchure
- [ ] breathing
- [ ] *D. C. al Fine*

EXERCISE 33
- [ ] notes/rhythm
- [ ] hand position
- [ ] dynamics
- [ ] tone

EXERCISE 35
- [ ] notes/rhythm
- [ ] breathing
- [ ] tempo
- [ ] tone

EXERCISE 36
- [ ] notes/rhythm
- [ ] posture
- [ ] embouchure
- [ ] tone

EXERCISE 39
- [ ] notes/rhythm
- [ ] embouchure
- [ ] dynamics
- [ ] *accelerando*

EXERCISE 42
- [ ] notes/rhythm
- [ ] hand position
- [ ] time signatures
- [ ] 𝄐

EXERCISE 45
- [ ] notes/rhythm
- [ ] hand position
- [ ] articulation
- [ ] tone

EXERCISE 47
- [ ] notes/rhythm
- [ ] posture
- [ ] tenuto
- [ ] tone

EXERCISE 51
- [ ] notes/rhythm
- [ ] hand position
- [ ] articulation
- [ ] tempo

EXERCISE 53
- [ ] notes/rhythm
- [ ] embouchure
- [ ] accents
- [ ] tempo

EXERCISE 57
- [ ] notes/rhythm
- [ ] hand position
- [ ] embouchure
- [ ] tone

EXERCISE 62
- [ ] notes/rhythm
- [ ] dynamics
- [ ] tenuto
- [ ] tempo

EXERCISE 65
- [ ] notes/rhythm
- [ ] posture
- [ ] articulations
- [ ] *D. C. al Fine*

EXERCISE 67
- [ ] notes/rhythm
- [ ] hand position
- [ ] embouchure
- [ ] tone

EXERCISE 69
- [ ] notes/rhythm
- [ ] hand position
- [ ] embouchure
- [ ] tone

EXERCISE 72
- [ ] notes/rhythm
- [ ] posture
- [ ] articulations
- [ ] breathing

EXERCISE 76
- [ ] notes/rhythm
- [ ] tempo
- [ ] legato
- [ ] tone

EXERCISE 77
- [ ] notes/rhythm
- [ ] hand position
- [ ] tempo
- [ ] tone

EXERCISE 81
- [ ] notes/rhythm
- [ ] hand position
- [ ] embouchure
- [ ] tone

EXERCISE 87
- [ ] notes/rhythm
- [ ] dynamics
- [ ] tone
- [ ] tempo

EXERCISE 88
- [ ] notes/rhythm
- [ ] hand position
- [ ] time signatures
- [ ] tonguing

EXERCISE 91
- [ ] notes/rhythm
- [ ] *D. C. al Coda*
- [ ] tempo
- [ ] tone

EXERCISE 92
- [ ] notes/rhythm
- [ ] hand position
- [ ] posture
- [ ] tone

EXERCISE 96
- [ ] notes/rhythm
- [ ] dynamics
- [ ] accents
- [ ] tonguing

EXERCISE 100
- [ ] notes/rhythm
- [ ] dynamics
- [ ] articulations
- [ ] tempo

EXERCISE 101
- [ ] notes/rhythm
- [ ] hand position
- [ ] posture
- [ ] tone

EXERCISE 106
- [ ] notes/rhythm
- [ ] accents
- [ ] tempo
- [ ] tone

EXERCISE 111
- [ ] notes/rhythm
- [ ] tempo
- [ ] posture
- [ ] tone

EXERCISE 115
- [ ] notes/rhythm
- [ ] hand position
- [ ] tempo
- [ ] accents

EXERCISE 116
- [ ] notes/rhythm
- [ ] time signatures
- [ ] tempo
- [ ] articulations

EXERCISE 118
- [ ] notes/rhythm
- [ ] articulations
- [ ] tempo
- [ ] tone

THE BB♭ TUBA

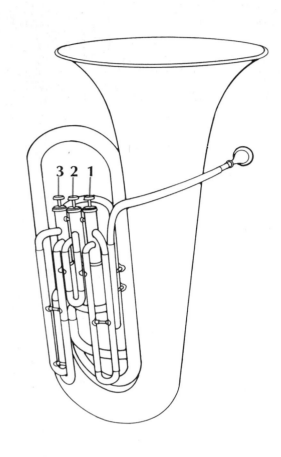

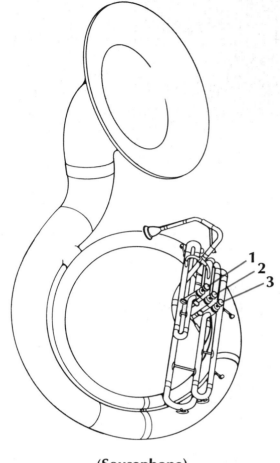

(Sousaphone)

TUBA CHECKLIST

☐ Sitting up straight

☐ Head erect

☐ Left hand and wrist position correct

☐ Right hand and wrist position correct

☐ Tuba correctly positioned in relation to body

☐ Fingers gently curved

☐ Elbows away from body

☐ Proper mouthpiece placement

☐ Corners of lips firm and center relaxed

☐ Chin flat and pointed

☐ Breathing properly

☐ Relaxed buzz

TUBA SURVIVAL KIT

☐ soft, clean cloth

☐ valve oil

☐ pencil

☐ band music

☐ mouthpiece cleaning brush

☐ slide grease

☐ method book

☐ music stand